MODERN CURSIVE HANDWRITING WORKBOOK

ALICE'S ADVENTURES IN WONDERLAND

75 Modern Cursive Handwriting Pages to Trace and Copy for Penmanship Practice

with Cursive Alphabet Review Pages

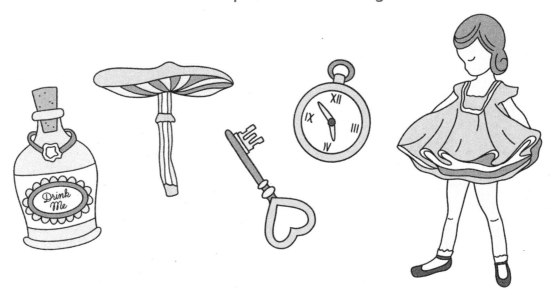

MOLLY SUBER THORPE

Author of *Modern Cursive Handwriting*
and *Mastering Modern Calligraphy*

MODERN CURSIVE HANDWRITING WORKBOOK:
ALICE'S ADVENTURES IN WONDERLAND
75 Modern Cursive Handwriting Pages to Trace and Copy for Penmanship Practice

Text of the traceable cursive passages is from
Alice's Adventures in Wonderland by Lewis Carroll (1895).
All other text by Molly Suber Thorpe.

Illustrations, layout, and cover design by Molly Suber Thorpe.

Digital typefaces: Sagona by René Bieder; Proxima Nova by Mark Simonson.

ISBN 979-8-9858650-9-7

First Edition: May 2023

Learn more about the author at: mollysuberthorpe.com

This book belongs to

What readers are saying about
Modern Cursive Handwriting:

I loved it so much that I decided to buy another copy and photocopy the pages to write on. This is perfect for someone who learned cursive in primary school but has since forgotten. I love writing in cursive now.

— ROSE H.

As someone who never picked up cursive in grade school, I feel certain I will be fluent at it by the end of this hearty book.

— ASHER

The details and quality of this book are out of this world. I was so pleased with the book the details and break down of how to do each letter and how to connect them I am buying another copy of this book [for] my little niece who is also trying to learn cursive writing. It is never too late to learn.

— AMAZON VERIFIED REVIEWER

Both comprehensive and easy to follow. The exercises build up from very basic to intermediate by the end. I recommend this for anyone looking to start or refresh their cursive skill.

— AMAZON VERIFIED REVIEWER

THE
MODERN CURSIVE HANDWRITING WORKBOOK
SERIES

Practice the cursive skills you learned from my bestselling *Modern Cursive Handwriting* with its companion workbooks!

Learn the fundamentals of cursive with the first book in the series: *Modern Cursive Handwriting*, featuring 200+ pages of exercises and beginner-friendly instruction.

Then continue improving your penmanship with my series of intermediate workbooks.

PENMANSHIP PRACTICE
FOR BEGINNERS AND BEYOND

More books

Modern Cursive Handwriting

A Step-by-Step Guide and Workbook to Learn
Script Penmanship for Adults and Teens

Trace-to-Learn Lettering Workbooks

A No-Frills Workbook Series for
Different Hand Lettering Styles

Modern Calligraphy

Everything You Need to Know
to Get Started in Script Calligraphy

Mastering Modern Calligraphy

Beyond the Basics: 2,700+ Pointed Pen Exemplars
and Exercises for Developing Your Style

Decorative Alphabets

A Coloring Book of Letters and Borders

The Calligrapher's Business Handbook

Pricing and Policies for Lettering Artists

Table of Contents

Alice's Adventures in Wonderland

Always speak the truth,
think before you speak, and
write it down afterwards.

Lewis Carroll

We learn penmanship not simply to produce individual letters, but to write whole sentences and full pages of words. Thus, there's no better way to practice and master cursive handwriting than by tracing and copying passages from books and other written works.

In the 75 practice pages that follow, you will improve your cursive by tracing and copying the first three chapters of Lewis Carroll's most beloved tale, *Alice's Adventures in Wonderland.*

Practice your penmanship by tracing each line of text on the traceable pages. Then, write the line again, this time freehand, in the blank guideline spaces underneath.

Share your progress on Instagram with the tag:
#SHAREMYSCRIPT

Tag me so I can have a peek:
@MOLLYSUBERTHORPE

How to use this workbook

Practice the cursive skills you learned from my step-by-step guide *Modern Cursive Handwriting* with this companion workbook.

Consider tracing or photocopying the pages.

I designed this workbook with the intent that each page could be practiced over and over again. Although you can write directly inside the book, you can also trace the cursive with tracing paper, or photocopy it for personal use. Tracing or photocopying will extend the life of the book, so you can revisit each exercise as many times as you need. In the final section, you will find blank guide sheets that you can easily cut out, trace, or photocopy.

Smaller handwriting may take more practice.

In the first book of this series, *Modern Cursive Handwriting*, I designed the guideline spaces slightly larger than what everyday applications of cursive usually require because medium-sized letters are easier to write slowly and deliberately – just what's needed when you're getting started.

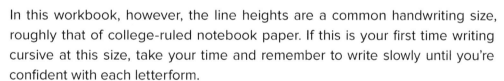

In this workbook, however, the line heights are a common handwriting size, roughly that of college-ruled notebook paper. If this is your first time writing cursive at this size, take your time and remember to write slowly until you're confident with each letterform.

Visit my website for links and downloads.

I invite you to visit my Modern Cursive Handwriting website for free resources, including printable lined paper, bonus practice sheets, and my favorite writing tools: **mollysuberthorpe.com/cursive**

Alphabet practice

CURSIVE REVIEW

In the following pages, you can refresh yourself on the cursive alphabet. Trace the letters slowly and carefully, then practice them freehand in the remaining space.

The first pages have large practice letters with arrows, for reviewing the stroke shapes and directions. The pages after that are for practicing a smaller handwriting size used in the book's practice pages.

Aa Bb Cc Dd Ee Ff
Gg Hh Ii Jj Kk
Ll Mm Nn Oo Pp
Qq Rr Ss Tt Uu
Vv Ww Xx Yy Zz

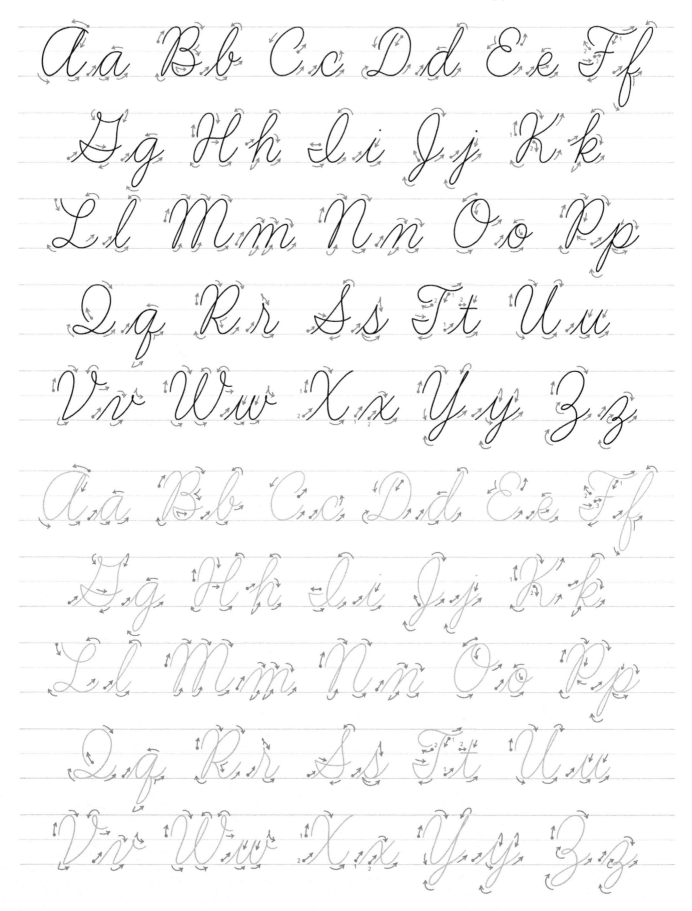

Aa Bb Cc Dd Ee Ff

Gg Hh Ii Jj Kk

Ll Mm Nn Oo Pp

Qq Rr Ss Tt Uu

Vv Ww Xx Yy Zz

Aa Bb Cc Dd Ee Ff

Gg Hh Ii Jj Kk

Ll Mm Nn Oo Pp

Qq Rr Ss Tt Uu

Vv Ww Xx Yy Zz

Aa Bb Cc Dd Ee Ff Gg Hh Ii
Jj Kk Ll Mm Nn Oo Pp Qq
Rr Ss Tt Uu Vv Ww Xx Yy Zz

Aa Bb Cc Dd Ee Ff Gg Hh Ii
Jj Kk Ll Mm Nn Oo Pp Qq
Rr Ss Tt Uu Vv Ww Xx Yy Zz

Aa Bb Cc Dd Ee Ff Gg Hh Ii
Jj Kk Ll Mm Nn Oo Pp Qq
Rr Ss Tt Uu Vv Ww Xx Yy Zz

Aa Bb Cc Dd Ee Ff Gg Hh Ii
Jj Kk Ll Mm Nn Oo Pp Qq
Rr Ss Tt Uu Vv Ww Xx Yy Zz

Aa Bb Cc Dd Ee Ff Gg Hh Ii
Jj Kk Ll Mm Nn Oo Pp Qq
Rr Ss Tt Uu Vv Ww Xx Yy Zz

Aa Bb Cc Dd Ee Ff Gg Hh Ii
Jj Kk Ll Mm Nn Oo Pp Qq
Rr Ss Tt Uu Vv Ww Xx Yy Zz

Alice's Adventures in Wonderland

BY

Lewis Carroll

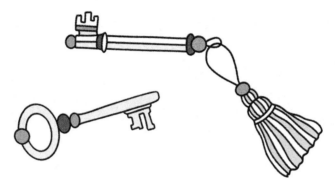

Chapter One
Down the Rabbit-Hole

Alice was beginning to get very tired of sitting by her sister on the bank, and of having nothing to do: once or twice she had peeped into the book her sister was reading, but it had no pictures or conversations in it, "and what is the use of a book," thought Alice "without pictures or conversations?"

So she was considering in her own mind (as well as she could, for the hot day made her feel very sleepy and stupid), whether the pleasure of making a daisy-chain would be worth the

trouble of getting up and picking the daisies,

when suddenly a White Rabbit with pink eyes

ran close by her.

There was nothing so very remarkable in that;

nor did Alice think it so very much out of the

way to hear the Rabbit say to itself, "Oh dear!

Oh dear! I shall be late!" (when she thought it

over afterwards, it occurred to her that she ought

to have wondered at this, but at the time it

all seemed quite natural); but when the Rabbit

actually took a watch out of its waistcoat-pocket,

and looked at it, and then hurried on, Alice

started to her feet, for it flashed across her mind

that she had never before seen a rabbit with

either a waistcoat-pocket, or a watch to take

out of it, and burning with curiosity, she ran

across the field after it, and fortunately was just

in time to see it pop down a large rabbit-hole

under the hedge.

In another moment down went Alice after

it, never once considering how in the world she

was to get out again.

The rabbit-hole went straight on like a tun-

nel for some way, and then dipped suddenly

down, so suddenly that Alice had not a moment

to think about stopping herself before she found

herself falling down a very deep well.

Either the well was very deep, or she fell very

slowly, for she had plenty of time as she went

down to look about her and to wonder what was

going to happen next. First, she tried to look down

and make out what she was coming to, but it

was too dark to see anything; then she looked at

the sides of the well, and noticed that they were

filled with cupboards and book-shelves; here and

there she saw maps and pictures hung upon pegs.

She took down a jar from one of the shelves as

she passed; it was labelled "Orange Marmalade,"

but to her great disappointment it was empty:

she did not like to drop the jar for fear of killing

somebody underneath, so managed to put it into

one of the cupboards as she fell past it.

"Well!" thought Alice to herself, "after such a

fall as this, I shall think nothing of tumbling

down stairs! How brave they'll all think me at

home! Why, I wouldn't say anything about it,

even if I fell off the top of the house!" (Which

was very likely true.)

Down, down, down. Would the fall never

come to an end? "I wonder how many miles

I've fallen by this time?" she said aloud. "I must

be getting somewhere near the centre of the earth.

Let me see: that would be four thousand miles

down, I think—" (for, you see, Alice had learnt

several things of this sort in her lessons in the

schoolroom, and though this was not a very

good opportunity for showing off her knowledge,

as there was no one to listen to her, still it was

good practice to say it over) "—yes, that's about

the right distance – but then I wonder what

Latitude or Longitude I've got to?" (Alice had

no idea what Latitude was, or Longitude either,

but thought they were nice grand words to say.)

Presently she began again. "I wonder if I

shall fall right through the earth! How funny

it'll seem to come out among the people that

walk with their heads downward! Antipathies,

I think –" (she was rather glad there was no

one listening, this time, as it didn't sound at

all the right word)" – but I shall have to ask

them what the name of the country is, you

know. Please, Ma'am, is this New Zealand

or Australia?" (and she tried to curtsey

as she spoke – fancy curtseying as you're

falling through the air! Do you think you

could manage it?) "And what an ignorant

little girl she'll think me for asking! No, it'll

never do to ask: perhaps I shall see it written

up somewhere."

Down, down, down. There was nothing else to do, so Alice soon began talking again. "Dinah'll miss me very much to-night, I should think!" (Dinah was the cat.) "I hope they'll remember her saucer of milk at tea-time. Dinah my dear! I wish you were down here with me! There are no mice in the air, I'm afraid, but you might catch a bat, and that's very like a mouse, you know. But do cats eat bats, I wonder?" And here Alice began to get rather sleepy, and went on saying to herself, in a dreamy sort of way,

"Do cats eat bats? Do cats eat bats?" and

sometimes, "Do bats eat cats?" for, you see, as

she couldn't answer either question, it didn't

much matter which way she put it. She felt

that she was dozing off, and had just begun

to dream that she was walking hand in hand

with Dinah, and saying to her very earnestly,

"Now, Dinah, tell me the truth: did you ever

eat a bat?" when suddenly, thump! thump!

down she came upon a heap of sticks and dry

leaves, and the fall was over.

　　Alice was not a bit hurt, and she jumped up

on to her feet in a moment: she looked up, but

it was all dark overhead; before her was another

long passage, and the White Rabbit was still

in sight, hurrying down it. There was not a

moment to be lost: away went Alice like the

wind, and was just in time to hear it say, as

it turned a corner, "Oh my ears and whiskers,

how late it's getting!" She was close behind it

when she turned the corner, but the Rabbit was

no longer to be seen: she found herself in a long,

low hall, which was lit up by a row of lamps

hanging from the roof.

There were doors all round the hall, but they

were all locked; and when Alice had been all the

way down one side and up the other, trying

every door, she walked sadly down the middle,

wondering how she was ever to get out again.

Suddenly she came upon a little three-legged table, all made of solid glass; there was nothing on it except a tiny golden key, and Alice's first thought was that it might belong to one of the doors of the hall; but, alas! either the locks were too large, or the key was too small, but at any rate it would not open any of them. However, on the second time round, she came upon a low curtain she had not noticed before, and behind it was a little door about fifteen inches high: she tried the little golden key in the lock, and to

her great delight it fitted!

Alice opened the door and found that it led

into a small passage, not much larger than

a rat-hole: she knelt down and looked along

the passage into the loveliest garden you ever

saw. How she longed to get out of that dark hall,

and wander about among those beds of bright

flowers and those cool fountains, but she could

not even get her head through the doorway;

"and even if my head would go through,"

thought poor Alice, "it would be of very little use

without my shoulders. Oh, how I wish I could

shut up like a telescope! I think I could, if I only

knew how to begin." For, you see, so many out-

of-the-way things had happened lately, that

Alice had begun to think that very few things

indeed were really impossible.

There seemed to be no use in waiting by the

little door, so she went back to the table, half

hoping she might find another key on it, or

at any rate a book of rules for shutting people

up like telescopes: this time she found a little

bottle on it, ("which certainly was not here

before," said Alice,) and round the neck of the

bottle was a paper label, with the words "Drink

Me," beautifully printed on it in large letters.

It was all very well to say "Drink Me," but

the wise little Alice was not going to do that in

a hurry. "No, I'll look first," she said, "and see

whether it's marked 'poison' or not;" for she had

read several nice little histories about children

who had got burnt, and eaten up by wild beasts

and other unpleasant things, all because they

would not remember the simple rules their

friends had taught them: such as, that a red-hot

poker will burn you if you hold it too long; and

that if you cut your finger very deeply with

a knife, it usually bleeds; and she had never

forgotten that, if you drink much from a bottle

marked "poison," it is almost certain to disagree

with you, sooner or later.

However, this bottle was not marked "poison," so

Alice ventured to taste it, and finding it very nice,

(it had, in fact, a sort of mixed flavour of cherry-

tart, custard, pine-apple, roast turkey, toffee, and

hot buttered toast,) she very soon finished it off.

"What a curious feeling!" said Alice; "I must

be shutting up like a telescope."

And so it was indeed: she was now only

ten inches high, and her face brightened up at

the thought that she was now the right size for

going through the little door into that lovely

garden. First, however, she waited for a few

minutes to see if she was going to shrink any

further: she felt a little nervous about this; "for

it might end, you know," said Alice to herself,

"in my going out altogether, like a candle. I

wonder what I should be like then?" And she

tried to fancy what the flame of a candle is like

after the candle is blown out, for she could not

remember ever having seen such a thing.

   After a while, finding that nothing more

happened, she decided on going into the garden

at once; but, alas for poor Alice! when she got

to the door, she found she had forgotten the little

golden key, and when she went back to the table

for it, she found she could not possibly reach it:

she could see it quite plainly through the glass,

and she tried her best to climb up one of the legs

of the table, but it was too slippery; and when

she had tired herself out with trying, the poor

little thing sat down and cried.

"Come, there's no use in crying like that!"

said Alice to herself, rather sharply; "I advise

you to leave off this minute!" She generally

gave herself very good advice, (though she very

seldom followed it), and sometimes she scolded

herself so severely as to bring tears into her eyes;

and once she remembered trying to box her

own ears for having cheated herself in a game

of croquet she was playing against herself, for

this curious child was very fond of pretending

to be two people. "But it's no use now," thought

poor Alice, "to pretend to be two people! Why,

there's hardly enough of me left to make one

respectable person!"

Soon her eye fell on a little glass box that was

lying under the table: she opened it, and found

in it a very small cake, on which the words

"Eat Me" were beautifully marked in currants.

"Well, I'll eat it," said Alice, "and if it makes

me grow larger, I can reach the key; and if it

makes me grow smaller, I can creep under the

door; so either way I'll get into the garden, and

I don't care which happens!"

She ate a little bit, and said anxiously to

herself, "Which way? Which way?" holding her

hand on the top of her head to feel which way

it was growing, and she was quite surprised to

find that she remained the same size: to be sure,

this generally happens when one eats cake, but

Alice had got so much into the way of expecting

nothing but out-of-the-way things to happen,

that it seemed quite dull and stupid for life to go

on in the common way.

So she set to work, and very soon finished

off the cake.

Chapter Two
The Pool of Tears

"Curiouser and curiouser!" cried Alice (she was

so much surprised, that for the moment she quite

forgot how to speak good English); "now I'm

opening out like the largest telescope that ever

was! Good-bye, feet!" (for when she looked down

at her feet, they seemed to be almost out of sight,

they were getting so far off). "Oh, my poor little

feet, I wonder who will put on your shoes and

stockings for you now, dears? I'm sure I shan't

be able! I shall be a great deal too far off to

trouble myself about you: you must manage

the best way you can; but I must be kind to

them," thought Alice, "or perhaps they won't

walk the way I want to go! Let me see: I'll

give them a new pair of boots every Christmas."

And she went on planning to herself how

she would manage it. "They must go by the

carrier," she thought; "and how funny it'll

seem, sending presents to one's own feet! And

how odd the directions will look!

Alice's Right Foot, Esq.,

Hearthrug, near the Fender,

(with Alice's love).

Oh dear, what nonsense I'm talking!"

Just then her head struck against the roof

of the hall: in fact she was now more than

nine feet high, and she at once took up the little

golden key and hurried off to the garden door.

Poor Alice! It was as much as she could do,

lying down on one side, to look through into

the garden with one eye; but to get through

was more hopeless than ever: she sat down and

began to cry again.

   "You ought to be ashamed of yourself," said

Alice, "a great girl like you," (she might well

say this), "to go on crying in this way! Stop

this moment, I tell you!" But she went on all

the same, shedding gallons of tears, until there

was a large pool all round her, about four inches

deep and reaching half down the hall.

After a time she heard a little pattering of feet in the distance, and she hastily dried her eyes to see what was coming. It was the White Rabbit returning, splendidly dressed, with a pair of white kid gloves in one hand and a large fan in the other: he came trotting along in a great hurry, muttering to himself as he came, "Oh! the Duchess, the Duchess! Oh! won't she be savage if I've kept her waiting!" Alice felt so desperate that she was ready to ask help of any one; so, when the Rabbit came

near her, she began, in a low, timid voice, "If you

please, sir—" The Rabbit started violently, dropped

the white kid gloves and the fan, and skurried

away into the darkness as hard as he could go.

Alice took up the fan and gloves, and, as the

hall was very hot, she kept fanning herself all

the time she went on talking: "Dear, dear! How

queer everything is to-day! And yesterday

things went on just as usual. I wonder if I've

been changed in the night? Let me think: was

I the same when I got up this morning? I

almost think I can remember feeling a little

different. But if I'm not the same, the next

question is, Who in the world am I? Ah, that's

the great puzzle!" And she began thinking

over all the children she knew that were of

the same age as herself, to see if she could

have been changed for any of them.

"I'm sure I'm not Ada," she said, "for her

hair goes in such long ringlets, and mine

doesn't go in ringlets at all; and I'm sure I

can't be Mabel, for I know all sorts of things,

and she, oh! she knows such a very little!

Besides, she's she, and I'm I, and — oh dear,

how puzzling it all is! I'll try if I know all the

things I used to know. Let me see: four times

five is twelve, and four times six is thirteen,

and four times seven is — oh dear! I shall

never get to twenty at that rate! However, the

Multiplication Table doesn't signify: let's try

Geography. London is the capital of Paris, and

Paris is the capital of Rome, and Rome — no,

that's all wrong, I'm certain! I must have

been changed for Mabel! I'll try and say

'How doth the little —'" and she crossed her

hands on her lap as if she were saying

lessons, and began to repeat it, but her voice

sounded hoarse and strange, and the words

did not come the same as they used to do: —

"How doth the little crocodile

Improve his shining tail,

And pour the waters of the Nile

On every golden scale!

How cheerfully he seems to grin,

How neatly spread his claws,

And welcome little fishes in

With gently smiling jaws!"

"I'm sure those are not the right words,"

said poor Alice, and her eyes filled with tears

again as she went on, "I must be Mabel after

all, and I shall have to go and live in that

poky little house, and have next to no toys to

play with, and oh! ever so many lessons to

learn! No, I've made up my mind about it; if

I'm Mabel, I'll stay down here! It'll be no use

their putting their heads down and saying 'Come

up again, dear!' I shall only look up and say

'Who am I then? Tell me that first, and then, if

I like being that person, I'll come up: if not, I'll

stay down here till I'm somebody else'—but, oh

dear!" cried Alice, with a sudden burst of tears, "I

do wish they would put their heads down! I am

so very tired of being all alone here!"

As she said this she looked down at her

hands, and was surprised to see that she had

put on one of the Rabbit's little white kid

gloves while she was talking. "How can I have

done that?" she thought. "I must be growing

small again." She got up and went to the table

to measure herself by it, and found that, as

nearly as she could guess, she was now about

two feet high, and was going on shrinking

rapidly: she soon found out that the cause of

this was the fan she was holding, and she

dropped it hastily, just in time to avoid

shrinking away altogether.

"That was a narrow escape!" said Alice, a good

deal frightened at the sudden change, but very

glad to find herself still in existence; "and now

for the garden!" and she ran with all speed

back to the little door: but, alas! the little door

was shut again, and the little golden key was

lying on the glass table as before, "and things

are worse than ever," thought the poor child,

"for I never was so small as this before, never!

And I declare it's too bad, that it is!"

As she said these words her foot slipped,

and in another moment, splash! she was up

to her chin in salt water. Her first idea was

that she had somehow fallen into the sea,

"and in that case I can go back by railway," she

said to herself. (Alice had been to the seaside

once in her life, and had come to the general

conclusion, that wherever you go to on the

English coast you find a number of bathing

machines in the sea, some children digging in

the sand with wooden spades, then a row of

lodging houses, and behind them a railway

station.) However, she soon made out that she

was in the pool of tears which she had wept

when she was nine feet high.

"I wish I hadn't cried so much!" said Alice,

as she swam about, trying to find her way out.

"I shall be punished for it now, I suppose, by

being drowned in my own tears! That will be

a queer thing, to be sure! However, everything

is queer to-day."

Just then she heard something splashing

about in the pool a little way off, and she

swam nearer to make out what it was: at first

she thought it must be a walrus or hippopotamus,

but then she remembered how small she was

now, and she soon made out that it was only

a mouse that had slipped in like herself.

"Would it be of any use, now," thought Alice,

"to speak to this mouse? Everything is so out-

of-the-way down here, that I should think

very likely it can talk: at any rate, there's

no harm in trying." So she began: "O Mouse,

do you know the way out of this pool? I am
very tired of swimming about here, O Mouse!"

(Alice thought this must be the right way of
speaking to a mouse: she had never done such
a thing before, but she remembered having
seen in her brother's Latin Grammar,"A mouse —
of a mouse — to a mouse — a mouse — O mouse!")

The Mouse looked at her rather inquisitively,
and seemed to her to wink with one of its
little eyes, but it said nothing.

"Perhaps it doesn't understand English," thought Alice; "I daresay it's a French mouse, come over with William the Conqueror." (For, with all her knowledge of history, Alice had no very clear notion how long ago anything had happened.) So she began again: "Où est ma chatte?" which was the first sentence in her French lessonbook. The Mouse gave a sudden leap out of the water, and seemed to quiver all over with fright. "Oh, I beg your pardon!"

cried Alice hastily, afraid that she had hurt

the poor animal's feelings. "I quite forgot you

didn't like cats."

"Not like cats!" cried the Mouse, in a shrill,

passionate voice. "Would you like cats if you

were me?"

"Well, perhaps not," said Alice in a soothing

tone: "don't be angry about it. And yet I

wish I could show you our cat Dinah: I think

you'd take a fancy to cats if you could only

see her. She is such a dear quiet thing," Alice

went on, half to herself, as she swam lazily about

in the pool, "and she sits purring so nicely by

the fire, licking her paws and washing her face —

and she is such a nice soft thing to nurse — and

she's such a capital one for catching mice — oh, I

beg your pardon!" cried Alice again, for this time

the Mouse was bristling all over, and she felt

certain it must be really offended. "We won't

talk about her any more if you'd rather not."

"We indeed!" cried the Mouse, who was trembling down to the end of his tail. "As if I would talk on such a subject! Our family always hated cats: nasty, low, vulgar things! Don't let me hear the name again!"

"I won't indeed!" said Alice, in a great hurry to change the subject of conversation. "Are you—are you fond—of—of dogs?" The Mouse did not answer, so Alice went on eagerly: "There is such a nice little dog near our house

I should like to show you! A little bright-eyed terrier, you know, with oh, such long curly brown hair! And it'll fetch things when you throw them, and it'll sit up and beg for its dinner, and all sorts of things — I can't remember half of them—and it belongs to a farmer, you know, and he says it's so useful, it's worth a hundred pounds! He says it kills all the rats and—oh dear!" cried Alice in a sorrowful tone, "I'm afraid I've offended it again!" For the Mouse was swimming away

from her as hard as it could go, and making

quite a commotion in the pool as it went.

So she called softly after it, "Mouse dear!

Do come back again, and we won't talk about

cats or dogs either, if you don't like them!"

When the Mouse heard this, it turned round

and swam slowly back to her: its face was quite

pale (with passion, Alice thought), and it said in

a low trembling voice, "Let us get to the shore,

and then I'll tell you my history, and you'll

understand why it is I hate cats and dogs."

 It was high time to go, for the pool was

getting quite crowded with the birds and

animals that had fallen into it: there were a

Duck and a Dodo, a Lory and an Eaglet, and

several other curious creatures. Alice led the

way, and the whole party swam to the shore.

Chapter Three
A Caucus-Race and a Long Tale

They were indeed a queer-looking party

that assembled on the bank — the birds with

draggled feathers, the animals with their fur

clinging close to them, and all dripping wet,

cross, and uncomfortable.

The first question of course was, how to get

dry again: they had a consultation about this,

and after a few minutes it seemed quite natural

to Alice to find herself talking familiarly with

them, as if she had known them all her life.

Indeed, she had quite a long argument with the Lory, who at last turned sulky, and would only say, "I am older than you, and must know better;" and this Alice would not allow without knowing how old it was, and, as the Lory positively refused to tell its age, there was no more to be said.

At last the Mouse, who seemed to be a person of authority among them, called out, "Sit down, all of you, and listen to me! I'll soon make you dry enough!" They all sat

down at once, in a large ring, with the Mouse

in the middle. Alice kept her eyes anxiously

fixed on it, for she felt sure she would catch a

bad cold if she did not get dry very soon.

"Ahem!" said the Mouse with an important

air, "are you all ready? This is the driest thing

I know. Silence all round, if you please!

'William the Conqueror, whose cause was fav-

oured by the pope, was soon submitted to by

the English, who wanted leaders, and had been

of late much accustomed to usurpation and

conquest. Edwin and Morcar, the earls of Mercia

and Northumbria — "

"Ugh!" said the Lory, with a shiver.

"I beg your pardon!" said the Mouse, frown-

ing, but very politely: "Did you speak?"

"Not I!" said the Lory hastily.

"I thought you did," said the Mouse. "—I

proceed. 'Edwin and Morcar, the earls of

Mercia and Northumbria, declared for him:

and even Stigand, the patriotic archbishop

of Canterbury, found it advisable—"

"Found what?" said the Duck.

"Found it," the Mouse replied rather crossly:

"of course you know what 'it' means."

"I know what 'it' means well enough, when

I find a thing," said the Duck: "it's generally

a frog or a worm. The question is, what did the

archbishop find?"

The Mouse did not notice this question, but hurriedly went on, "'—found it advisable to go with Edgar Atheling to meet William and offer him the crown. William's conduct at first was moderate. But the insolence of his Normans—' How are you getting on now, my dear?" it continued, turning to Alice as it spoke.

"As wet as ever," said Alice in a melancholy tone: "it doesn't seem to dry me at all."

"In that case," said the Dodo solemnly,

rising to its feet, "I move that the meeting

adjourn, for the immediate adoption of more

energetic remedies—"

"Speak English!" said the Eaglet. "I don't know

the meaning of half those long words, and,

what's more, I don't believe you do either!"

And the Eaglet bent down its head to hide a

smile: some of the other birds tittered audibly.

"What I was going to say," said the Dodo

in an offended tone, "was, that the best thing

to get us dry would be a Caucus-race."

"What is a Caucus-race?" said Alice; not

that she wanted much to know; but the Dodo

had paused as if it thought that somebody

ought to speak, and no one else seemed

inclined to say anything.

"Why," said the Dodo, "the best way to

explain it is to do it." (And, as you might like

to try the thing yourself, some winter day, I

will tell you how the Dodo managed it.)

First it marked out a race-course, in a sort of circle, ("the exact shape doesn't matter," it said,) and then all the party were placed along the course, here and there. There was no "One, two, three, and away," but they began running when they liked, and left off when they liked, so that it was not easy to know when the race was over. However, when they had been running half an hour or so, and were quite dry again, the Dodo suddenly called out

"The race is over!" and they all crowded round

it, panting, and asking, "But who has won?"

This question the Dodo could not answer

without a great deal of thought, and it sat for

a long time with one finger pressed upon its

forehead (the position in which you usually

see Shakespeare, in the pictures of him), while

the rest waited in silence. At last the Dodo said,

"Everybody has won, and all must have prizes."

"But who is to give the prizes?" quite a

chorus of voices asked.

"Why, she, of course," said the Dodo, pointing

to Alice with one finger; and the whole party

at once crowded round her, calling out in a

confused way, "Prizes! Prizes!"

Alice had no idea what to do, and in despair

she put her hand in her pocket, and pulled out

a box of comfits, (luckily the salt water had not

got into it), and handed them round as prizes.

There was exactly one a-piece, all round.

"But she must have a prize herself, you

know," said the Mouse.

"Of course," the Dodo replied very gravely.

"What else have you got in your pocket?" he

went on, turning to Alice.

"Only a thimble," said Alice sadly.

"Hand it over here," said the Dodo.

Then they all crowded round her once more,

while the Dodo solemnly presented the thimble,

saying "We beg your acceptance of this elegant

thimble;" and, when it had finished this short

speech, they all cheered.

Alice thought the whole thing very absurd,

but they all looked so grave that she did not

dare to laugh; and, as she could not think of

anything to say, she simply bowed, and took

the thimble, looking as solemn as she could.

The next thing was to eat the comfits: this

caused some noise and confusion, as the large

birds complained that they could not taste

theirs, and the small ones choked and had to

be patted on the back. However, it was over at

last, and they sat down again in a ring, and

begged the Mouse to tell them something more.

"You promised to tell me your history, you

know," said Alice, "and why it is you hate—C

and D," she added in a whisper, half afraid

that it would be offended again.

"Mine is a long and a sad tale!" said the

Mouse, turning to Alice, and sighing.

"It is a long tail, certainly," said Alice, looking

down with wonder at the Mouse's tail; "but why

do you call it sad?" And she kept on puzzling

about it while the Mouse was speaking, so that

her idea of the tale was something like this: —

"Fury said to a mouse,
That he met in the
house, 'Let us both
go to law: I will
prosecute you.
— Come, I'll
take no denial;
We must have
the trial: For
really this
morning I've
nothing to do.'
Said the mouse
to the cur, 'Such
a trial, dear sir,
With no jury
or judge, would
be wasting our
breath.' 'I'll be
judge, I'll be
jury,' Said
cunning
old Fury:
'I'll try
the whole
cause, and
condemn
you to
death.'"

"You are not attending!" said the Mouse to Alice severely. "What are you thinking of?"

"I beg your pardon," said Alice very humbly:

"you had got to the fifth bend, I think?"

"I had not!" cried the Mouse, sharply and very angrily.

"A knot!" said Alice, always ready to make herself useful, and looking anxiously about her.

"Oh, do let me help to undo it!"

"I shall do nothing of the sort," said the

Mouse, getting up and walking away. "You

insult me by talking such nonsense!"

"I didn't mean it!" pleaded poor Alice. "But

you're so easily offended, you know!"

The Mouse only growled in reply.

"Please come back and finish your story!"

Alice called after it; and the others all joined

in chorus, "Yes, please do!" but the Mouse

only shook its head impatiently, and walked a

little quicker.

"What a pity it wouldn't stay!" sighed the

Lory, as soon as it was quite out of sight; and

an old Crab took the opportunity of saying

to her daughter "Ah, my dear! Let this be

a lesson to you never to lose your temper!"

"Hold your tongue, Ma!" said the young Crab,

a little snappishly. "You're enough to try the

patience of an oyster!"

"I wish I had our Dinah here, I know I

do!" said Alice aloud, addressing nobody in

particular. "She'd soon fetch it back!"

"And who is Dinah, if I might venture to ask the question?" said the Lory.

Alice replied eagerly, for she was always ready to talk about her pet: "Dinah's our cat. And she's such a capital one for catching mice you can't think! And oh, I wish you could see her after the birds! Why, she'll eat a little bird as soon as look at it!"

This speech caused a remarkable sensation

among the party. Some of the birds hurried

off at once: one old Magpie began wrapping

itself up very carefully, remarking, "I really

must be getting home; the night-air doesn't suit

my throat!" and a Canary called out in a

trembling voice to its children, "Come away, my

dears! It's high time you were all in bed!" On

various pretexts they all moved off, and Alice

was soon left alone.

"I wish I hadn't mentioned Dinah!" she said

to herself in a melancholy tone. "Nobody seems

to like her, down here, and I'm sure she's the best

cat in the world! Oh, my dear Dinah! I wonder

if I shall ever see you any more!" And here poor

Alice began to cry again, for she felt very lonely

and low-spirited. In a little while, however, she

again heard a little pattering of footsteps in the

distance, and she looked up eagerly, half hoping

that the Mouse had changed his mind, and was

coming back to finish his story.

Guide Sheets

CUT OUT, TRACE, PHOTOCOPY, PRINT

The following pages are blank guideline sheets in various opacities. The darker the lines, the easier they will be to see through tracing paper. If you're writing directly on the guide sheet, choose the lightest lines.

I recommend that you reuse these guides again and again by either photocopying them or placing tracing paper on top. You can follow the dashed lines to easily cut out the pages.

Need more? Download free printable guides at:

mollysuberthorpe.com/cursive

About the author

Molly Suber Thorpe creates custom lettering for brands and individuals around the world, digital assets for artists, and bestselling books for calligraphers.

Since 2009, Molly has helped letterers hone their skills — through her books, classes, and tools — opening doors to new creative opportunities and careers.

Molly is credited as a driving force behind the modern calligraphy movement, being among the first artists to use the whimsical, unorthodox pointed pen styles and bold color palettes so popular today.

She's had the privilege of working with clients including Google Arts & Culture, Michael Kors, Martha Stewart, Lonely Planet, and Fendi. Her work and words have been featured in such publications as The Guardian, The Wall Street Journal, Martha Stewart Weddings, Los Angeles Times, and Buzzfeed.

Molly also loves to teach. In addition to conducting in-person calligraphy workshops in the United States and Europe as her time permits, Molly is a Skillshare Top Teacher whose courses have been viewed by over 40,000 students.

In 2016, Molly founded Calligrafile.com, a free database of resources and products for calligraphers, lettering artists, type enthusiasts, and creative freelancers. It is the largest site of its kind, with over two dozen contributing artists, and thousands of users around the world.

TRACE-TO-LEARN LETTERING

Want to learn more styles of hand lettering?

Trace-to-Learn Lettering is a no-frills workbook
series for learning styles from brush script
to flourished calligraphy.

Learn more at:

TRACE-TO-LEARN.COM

Molly Suber Thorpe

FREE PRACTICE SHEETS

mollysletteringtoolkit.com

TUTORIALS

mollysuberthorpe.com/videos

MORE BOOKS

mollysuberthorpe.com/books

SOCIAL

@mollysuberthorpe

YOUTUBE

MollySuberThorpeLetters